The Mind
bender
VOLUME 2
Book
D0027082

The Mind bender Book

VOLUME 2

Another collection of favorites from the most popular radio contest in the world!

Dom Testa

ILLUSTRATIONS BY

Matt Lupton

Profound Impact Group, Inc.

The Mindbender Book
Volume 2

First Edition

Illustrations by Matt Lupton
Interior and cover design by Rebecca Finkel, F+P Graphic Design

For information, please write to:
Profound Impact Group, Inc., PO Box 370567, Denver, CO 80237

Library of Congress Control Number: 2011933432

ISBN: 978-0-9760564-9-2

Printed in Canada

The Mindbender Returns!

Celebrating its 20th anniversary on my morning radio show, the Mindbender has become an even bigger smash hit as people listen online or on their smartphones. Many others discovered it by picking up *The Mindbender Book, Volume 1* for themselves or for their friends and family.

I'm often asked to name the Mindbender that caused the biggest reaction. Well, it was long ago (January 25, 1994 to be exact), but I remember the screams of agony to this day. The question was:

What's the first thing you know?

Guesses ranged from "how to breathe," to "your mother's love," to "weightlessness" (I really liked that one). So imagine the groans when I finally gave the answer: Ol' Jed's a millionaire.

You'd have to be old enough to remember a television show called *The Beverly Hillbillies* (remember, I did this Mindbender in 1994), but to this day I still have people who bring up this classic moment and laugh. Don't get it? Ask an old person.

Some Mindbenders simply don't survive the test of time. For instance, in the mid-90s I offered this one:

Its annual revenue is about $3000...

The answer was: A pay phone. Good luck even finding a pay phone today!

So here's a fresh batch of classic Mindbenders, and another chance for you to compete with friends, family members, and co-workers. As with the first volume, there are blanks spaces provided for you and your rivals to jot down your guesses.

The answers are not in the back. Instead, I've placed each one a few pages ahead, near the bottom of the page. For example, the answer to number one is located below question number four. That way you won't "accidentally" see any of the next answers.

Once again sales of this new *Mindbender Book* will benefit my non-profit foundation that helps students recognize that Smart Is Cool. It's called The Big Brain Club (BigBrainClub.com), and more information is in the back of the book. Thanks for your support!

For copies of Volume 1, log on to DomTesta.com and we'll ship one right to your door.

Okay, it's time to get rolling with *The Mindbender Book, Volume 2.* Good luck!

1

Researchers say this is the food most commonly craved by pregnant women.

(Answer on page 4)

2

Since the fall of communism, this has been Russia's #1 import from America.

(Answer on page 5)

3

Experts say that to do this properly, you need 2½ inches of water.

answers

(Answer on page 6)

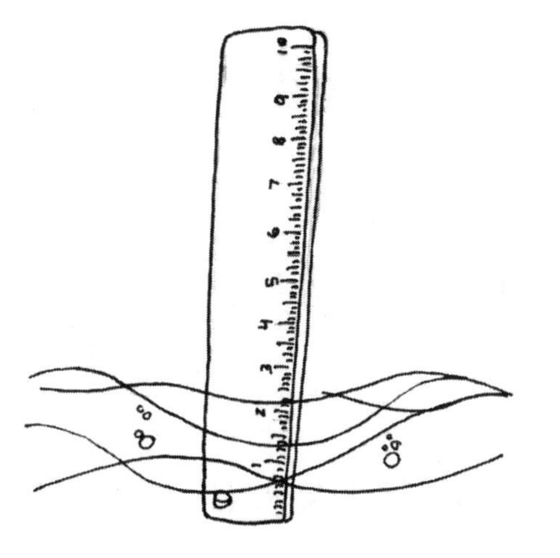

4

This is the most common high school nickname in the country.

(Answer on page 7)

MindBender 1: Nachos

5

There are about 5,400 calories in one of these.

answers

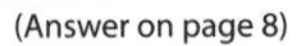

(Answer on page 8)

6

A survey of bosses found this to be the thing most likely to get you fired.

(Answer on page 9)

MindBender 3: Fill a bird bath

7

Research shows that almost half of Americans spend about 15 minutes of their work day doing this.

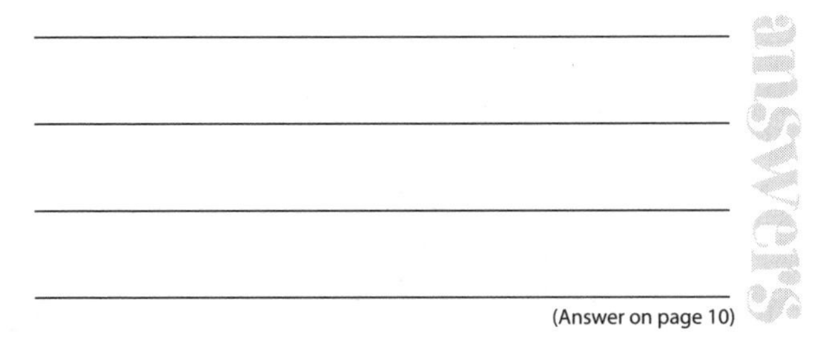

(Answer on page 10)

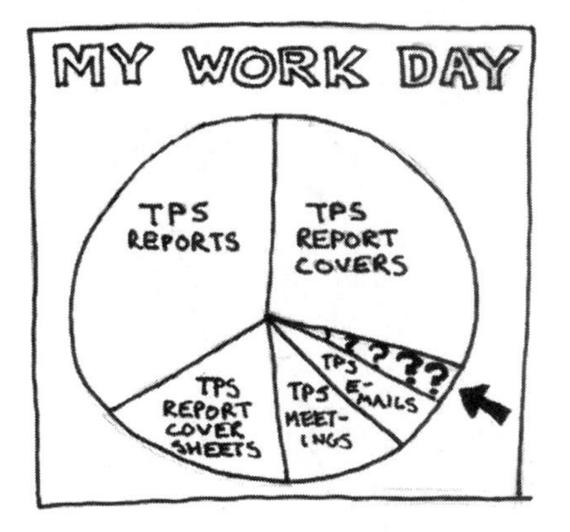

8

If you're an average person,
you will do this 90 times today.

(Answer on page 11)

answers

MindBender 5: An average trick-or-treat bag of Halloween candy

9

One in four married people have done this at least once since their wedding.

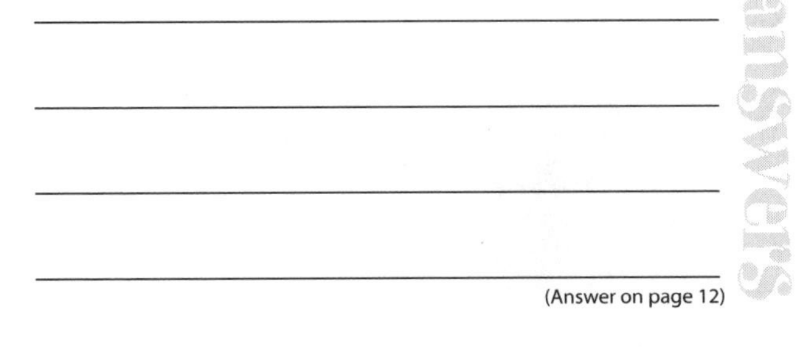

answers

(Answer on page 12)

MindBender 6: Frequent sick days

10

The three inanimate objects that figure most frequently in injuries are bicycles, stairs, and _______.

answers

(Answer on page 13)

11

The average American will eat enough of this in their lifetime to fill the backs of three pick-up trucks.

answers

(Answer on page 14)

12

This prediction is made thousands of times per day, but is wrong 96% of the time.

(Answer on page 15)

MindBender 9: Lost their wedding ring

13

Twenty-nine percent of people have misplaced their keys here.

answers

(Answer on page 16)

MindBender 10: Footballs

14

When it comes to their wallets, 72% of people have this in common.

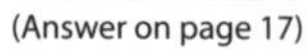
(Answer on page 17)

15

20,000 kids in America will be treated in emergency rooms this year when they get hurt by one of these.

(Answer on page 18)

answers

MindBender 12: A woman's due date

16

The average man will lose about one pound per year doing this.

(Answer on page 19)

MindBender 13: The front door lock

17

Thirty-one percent of American women clean this every day.

answers

(Answer on page 20)

MindBender 14: They keep their currency in sequence

According to pet experts, the best kind of dog a guy can have to attract a woman is a mini Doberman Pinscher. What type of dog came in second?

(Answer on page 21)

MindBender 15: Shopping carts

The average American woman spends 170 hours per year doing this.

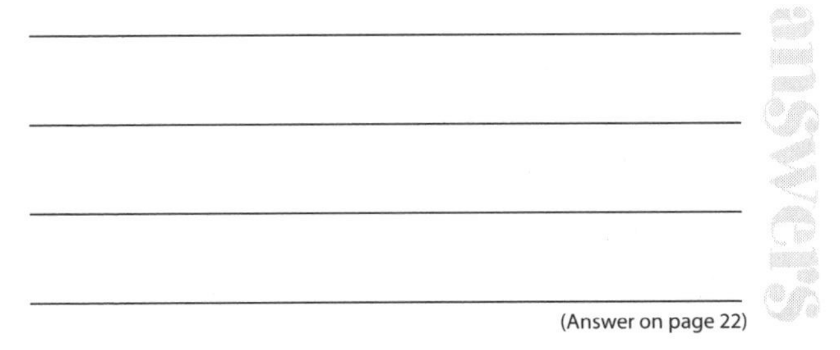

(Answer on page 22)

MindBender 16: Shaving

20

The average lifespan of one of these is about 18 months.

(Answer on page 23)

answers

MindBender 17: Their bellybutton

Sixteen percent of office workers in America admit to doing this at work.

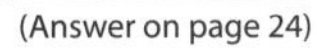

(Answer on page 24)

answers

MindBender 18: A beagle

It takes an average of three minutes, eight seconds to accomplish this.

____

____

____

____

(Answer on page 25)

answers

MindBender 19: Deciding what to wear

23

Thirty-seven percent of Americans say they have done this accidentally at night.

(Answer on page 26)

MindBender 20: A dollar bill

In a recent survey, four percent of people avoid going here because they are afraid of other people's germs.

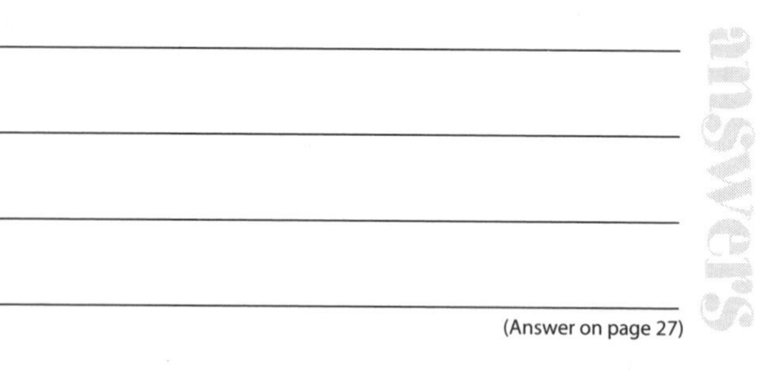

(Answer on page 27)

MindBender 21: Steal co-workers' food from the fridge

They average 5'9" in height, and 218 pounds in weight.

answers

(Answer on page 28)

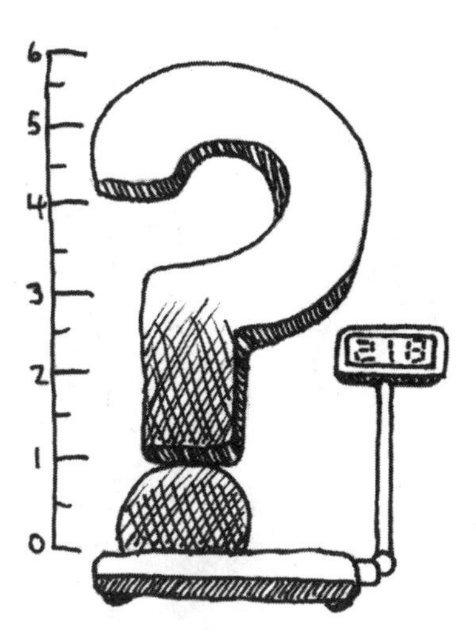

MindBender 22: Go through a fast-food drive-thru

26

One of these usually travels about eight miles per year.

answers

(Answer on page 29)

MindBender 23: Injured their spouse in their sleep

Seven out of 10 men say they do this without their spouse's knowledge.

answers

(Answer on page 30)

MindBender 24: Movie theaters

According to a survey, 27% of American men think that getting one of these will improve their love life.

____

____

____

____

(Answer on page 31)

MindBender 25: Shopping mall Santas

29

Sixty-four percent of Americans can't remember this.

(Answer on page 32)

answers

Six times more women than men will do this in the mornings.

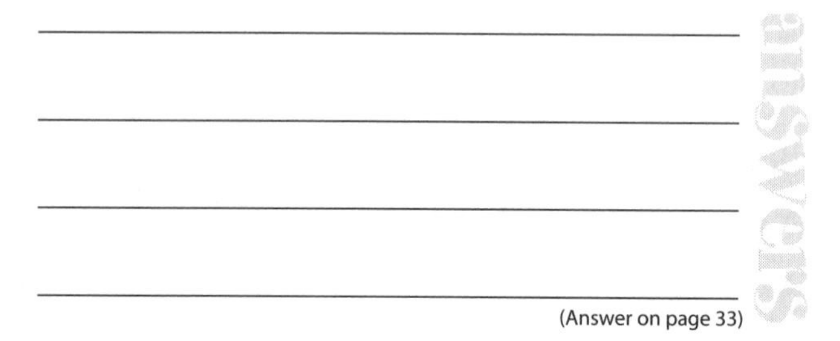

(Answer on page 33)

MindBender 27: Read their 'chick' magazines

You will probably do this 15 times today. Your kids will do it up to 400 times.

answers

(Answer on page 34)

32

The average kid will go through 730 of these by age 10.

____

____

____

____

answers

(Answer on page 35)

MindBender 29: What their spouse got them for Christmas last year

Fifty-one percent of us have never, ever washed this.

answers

(Answer on page 36)

MindBender 30: Hit the snooze button

34

Most of us have one of these. Seven percent of us have two of them.

(Answer on page 37)

This happens more in September than in any other month—more than 11,000 times each day.

answers

(Answer on page 38)

36

On average, these last about 10 days.

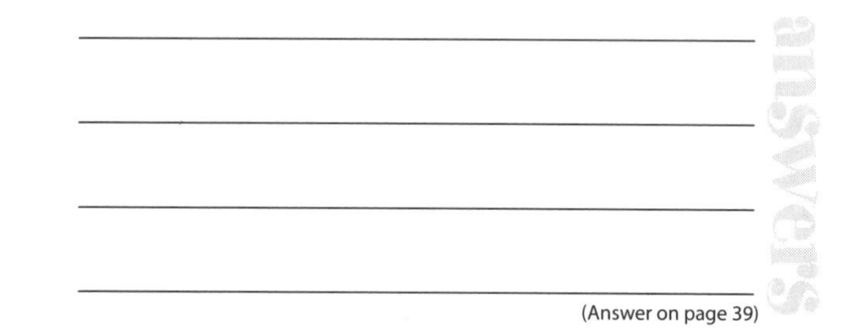

(Answer on page 39)

MindBender 33: Their pillow

37

Nine million people in America threw a party last year to celebrate this.

answers

(Answer on page 40)

MindBender 34: A middle name

The average woman has had seven of these in the last 10 years.

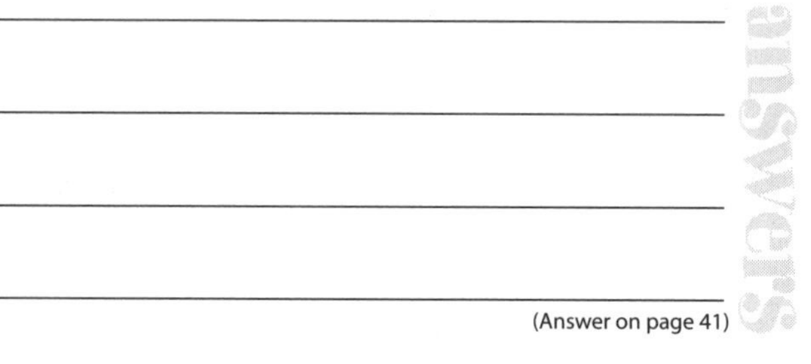

(Answer on page 41)

answers

MindBender 35: A baby is born

Five percent of Americans will do this on Christmas day.

answers

(Answer on page 42)

MindBender 36: A hurricane

40

On average, these will only last about 150 days.

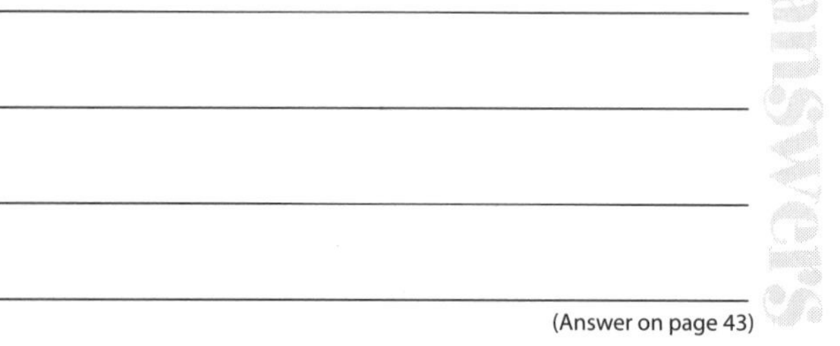

(Answer on page 43)

answers

MindBender 37: Their dog's birthday

These normally move at seven miles per hour.

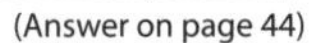

(Answer on page 44)

answers

Forty-two percent of Americans say they have never experienced this.

(Answer on page 45)

Twenty-two percent of women do this in the kitchen, compared to 40% of men.

answers

(Answer on page 46)

44

One in four Americans do not know this about themselves.

answers

(Answer on page 47)

A nationwide poll of homeowners found this to be their biggest regret about their house.

(Answer on page 48)

MindBender 42: Déjà vu

46

There are usually an average of 188 people here.

answers

(Answer on page 49)

MindBender 43: Drink straight from the container

It's estimated that 60% of these in American households don't work.

answers

(Answer on page 50)

MindBender 44: Their astrological sign

A survey found that six percent of people said they like to order this when they go out to eat, because they never have it at home.

answers

(Answer on page 51)

MindBender 45: Having (or installing) a pool

If you're going to buy one of these, statistics show that you're most likely to do it on Saturday morning, around 11 o'clock.

answers

(Answer on page 52)

50

Forty percent of women say they have done this in an attempt to impress someone.

answers

(Answer on page 53)

51

According to the FBI, 70% of these are fake.

answers

____

____

____

____

(Answer on page 54)

MindBender 48: Salad

Research shows that men with this physical feature tend to be smarter.

(Answer on page 55)

53

In your lifetime, you will probably eat 2,223 of these... and they're red.

answers

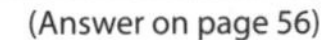
(Answer on page 56)

MindBender 50: Claimed they made food that they actually bought

54

Four in 10 women say this is what they dread the most.

answers

(Answer on page 57)

MindBender 51: Sports memorabilia autographs

55

Thirty-five percent of women say this is the best thing about pregnancy.

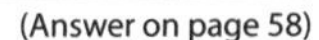

answers

(Answer on page 58)

MindBender 52: A hairy chest

Thirteen percent of workers say that they would be willing to take a pay cut if they could do this.

(Answer on page 59)

MindBender 53: Red M&Ms

Experts predict that this cost American businesses about $175 million in lost productivity last year.

answers

(Answer on page 60)

MindBender 54: Trying on clothes at the store

The very first one had a top speed of six miles per hour.

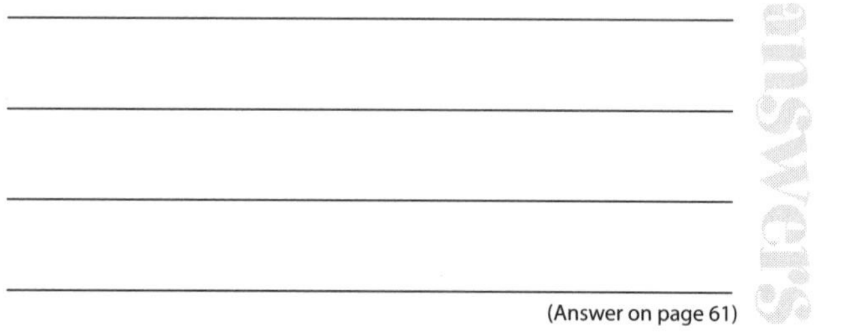

(Answer on page 61)

Americans throw away 570 of these every second. That's about 49 million each day.

answers

(Answer on page 62)

MindBender 56: Take their dog to work

60

The average adult spends four minutes, 20 seconds per day on this.

answers

(Answer on page 63)

MindBender 57: The NCAA basketball brackets

61

Thirty-one percent of Americans know a woman who has done this.

answers

(Answer on page 64)

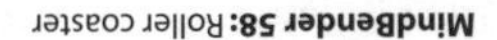
MindBender 58: Roller coaster

Thirteen percent of people who go to Las Vegas visit one of these.

answers

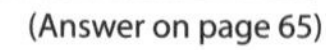

(Answer on page 65)

MindBender 59: Diapers

63

Studies show that women are more likely than men to call their spouse this.

answers

(Answer on page 66)

64

According to a survey, one-third of American workers would like for their company to allow this.

(Answer on page 67)

MindBender 61: Proposed marriage

65

Research shows that this is the most common morning habit.

(Answer on page 68)

MindBender 62: A pawn shop

66

The average American worker spends 5½ hours each week doing this.

(Answer on page 69)

MindBender 63: Their pet's name

67

Ten percent of single men say they have never done this.

answers

(Answer on page 70)

MindBender 64: Daily naps

Sixty-five percent of men and 60% percent of women said you should never do this until at least the third date.

answers

(Answer on page 71)

MindBender 65: Listening to the radio

69

At Christmas time, the average child will do this for 37 seconds.

answers

(Answer on page 72)

MindBender 66: Sitting in meetings

Fifty-one million people in America will be doing this today.

(Answer on page 73)

answers

You'll find one of these in 45% of the closets in America.

answers

(Answer on page 74)

MindBender 68: Talk about politics

Unfortunately, the average person will experience this 140 times in their lifetime.

____

____

____

____

(Answer on page 75)

MindBender 69: Sit on Santa's lap

Researchers say that a man who does this every morning typically makes more money than men who don't.

(Answer on page 76)

74

Women were asked what they feared the most about growing old, and 10% said this.

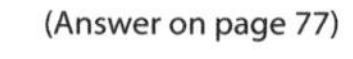

(Answer on page 77)

MindBender 71: Clothes with a sports team's logo

Seven percent of burglars have this in common.

(Answer on page 78)

76

Seventy-eight percent of Americans have one, but say that it rarely works.

(Answer on page 79)

answers

After money, this is the top reward that employers give to their employees.

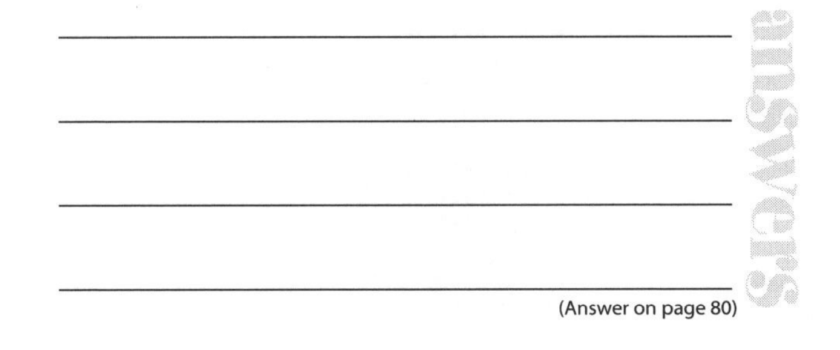

(Answer on page 80)

MindBender 74: Turning into their mother

78

The average American will visit one of these 233 times in their life.

____

____

____

____

(Answer on page 81)

MindBender 75: They watch TV while burglarizing the house

79

A survey asked men to name the oldest thing they have, and this was the top answer.

(Answer on page 82)

answers

Twenty-eight percent of men and 59% of women say they have kept this a secret from their significant other.

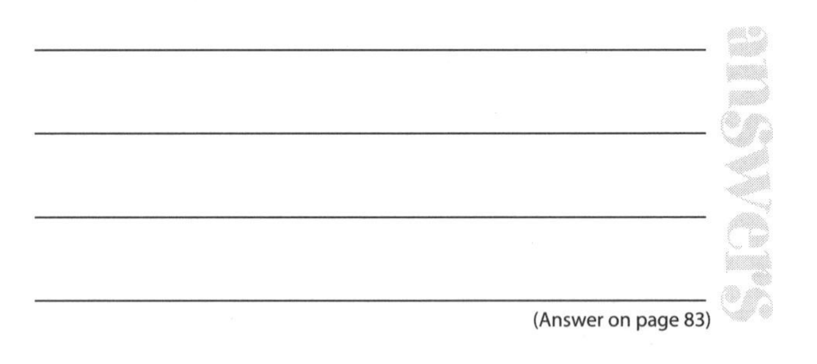

(Answer on page 83)

Thirty-eight percent of us do not have one of these. They're cheap, but not having one could cost you plenty.

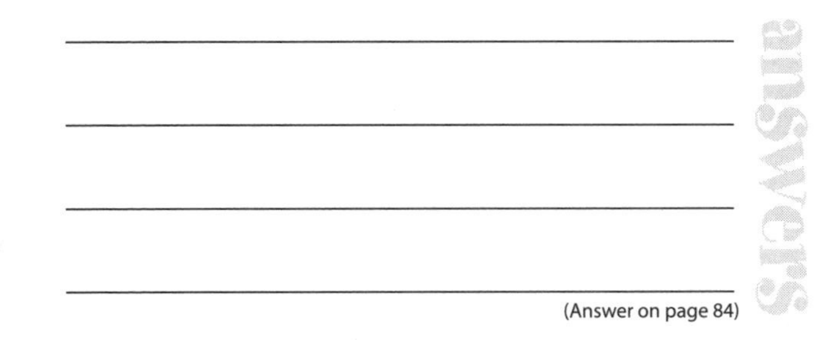

(Answer on page 84)

MindBender 78: A bowling alley

A survey found this to be the thing that irritates motorists the most.

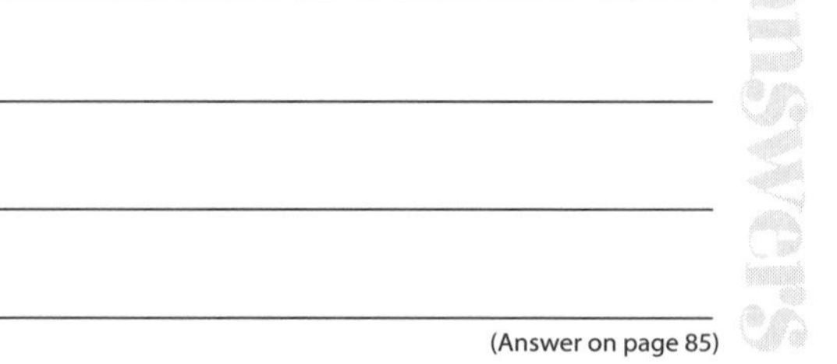

(Answer on page 85)

MindBender 79: A baseball glove

83

This measures 2¼ inches by 2¼ inches.

answers

(Answer on page 86)

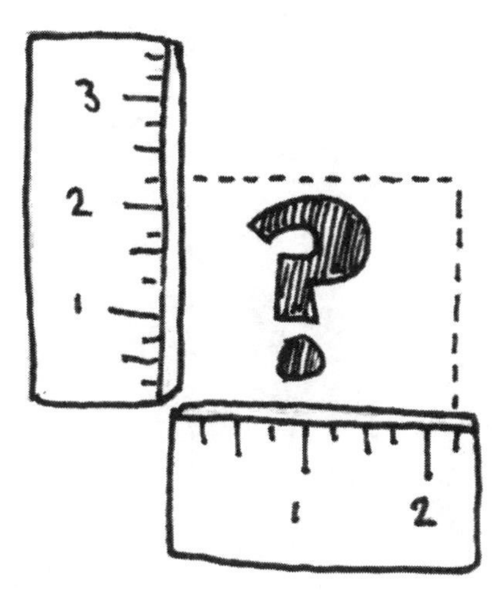

MindBender 80: A loan to a relative

Four percent of fathers will get this as a Father's Day gift this year.

answers

(Answer on page 87)

MindBender 81: Spare car key

According to a survey of bartenders, people in this profession are the worst tippers.

____

____

____

____

(Answer on page 88)

MindBender 82: People on bicycles

Americans will consume
42 tons of this today.

answers

(Answer on page 89)

MindBender 83: A Hershey's Kiss wrapper

87

The average one moves at about 1.17 miles per hour.

answers

(Answer on page 90)

MindBender 84: Nothing

A survey found that 22% percent of adults say this was the first person they feared in their lives.

(Answer on page 91)

MindBender 85: Doctors

Research shows that almost half of all products returned to a store due to a malfunction have this problem.

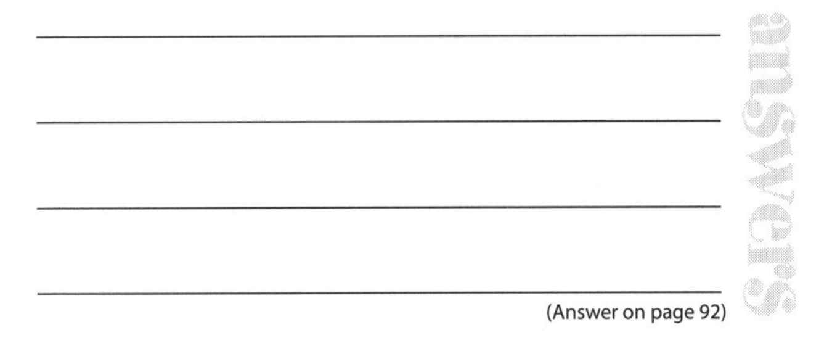

(Answer on page 92)

MindBender 86: Aspirin

If you're getting married soon, you should know that there's an 11% chance that this will happen to you.

(Answer on page 93)

answers

MindBender 87: A spider

A survey asked people to name the symbol which best represents the United States, and three percent of people said this.

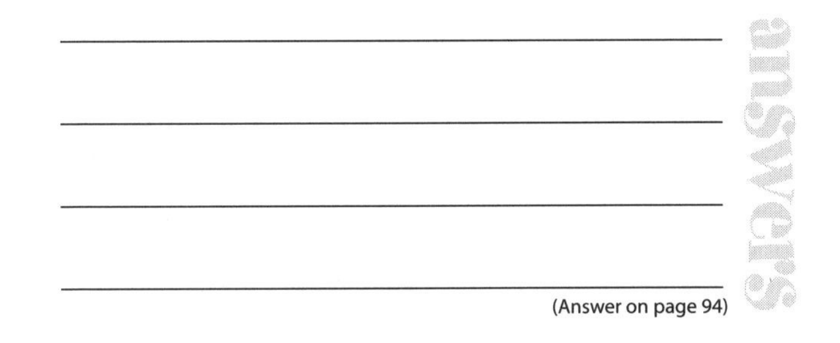

answers

(Answer on page 94)

MindBender 88: A nun

When going to the restroom at the office, 30% of men will do this, but only 12% of women will.

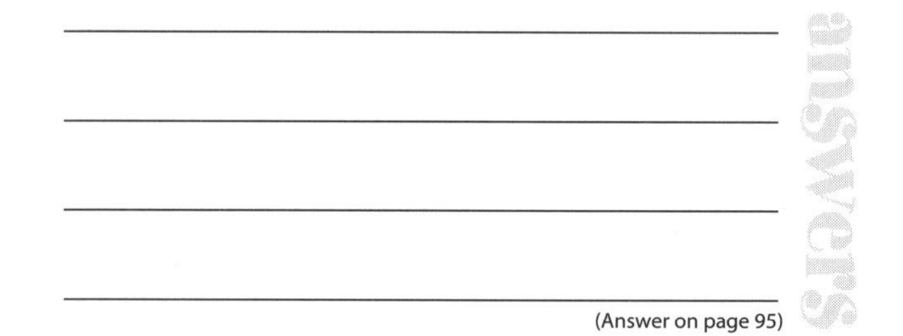

(Answer on page 95)

MindBender 89: Nothing

93

Ten percent of people can claim to have had one of these for at least 10 years.

(Answer on page 96)

answers

MindBender 90: Your mother or mother-in-law will move in

This occupation has the highest concentration of females, with men accounting for less than two percent.

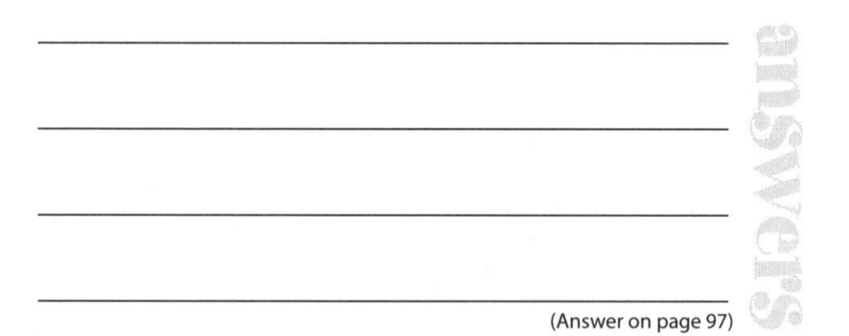

(Answer on page 97)

answers

MindBender 91: The McDonald's arches

Each of these is about 13½ inches tall and weighs 8½ pounds.

answers

(Answer on page 98)

MindBender 92: Leave if someone is already in one of the stalls

A recent survey of women found this to be the most intriguing trait in a potential husband.

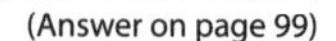
(Answer on page 99)

answers

MindBender 93: A pair of underwear

97

The average American will go through eight pounds of this every year.

answers

(Answer on page 100)

Twenty percent of Americans say they have a lucky ___________.

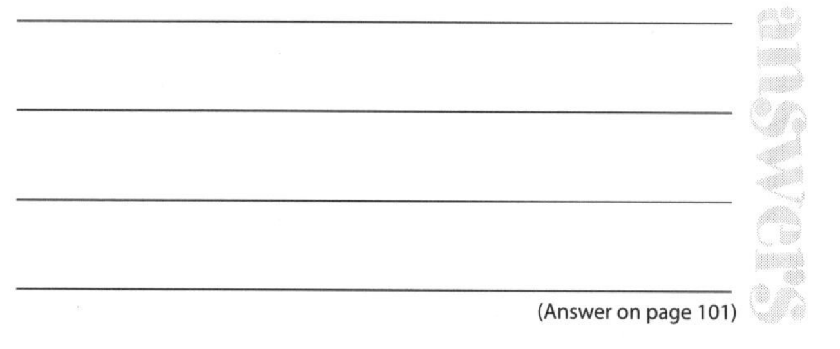

(Answer on page 101)

MindBender 95: The Oscar statuette from the Academy Awards

99

The average woman will spend two weeks of her life doing this.

answers

(Answer on page 102)

MindBender 96: Being an accomplished cook

A survey asked people who they would most want to have with them if they were stranded on a desert island. More than half the people said this.

answers

(Answer on page 103)

MindBender 97: Toilet paper

By purchasing this book, you've helped to support

BIG BRAIN CLUB

BCB

My passion is helping young people recognize that *Smart Is Cool.* Sadly, too many students intentionally dumb down because they fear being labeled a nerd or a dork. They desperately want to be considered one of the "cool" kids. But the day they leave high school they get a cold reality slap: suddenly, nobody cares how cool you were in school. Now all anyone cares about is what you know and what you can do.

The Big Brain Club is not about straight A's (although we love that!). It's about helping young people become the best version of themselves, and that begins with a solid education. Politicians, parent groups, and school administrators can argue all day about how to "fix" schools, but we're spinning our wheels—until the students shift their perception of education.

The foundation also provides cool technology to schools and publishes the creative writing of students. Additionally, we're a clearinghouse for teacher lesson plans and video programs that celebrate student achievement. Learn more about us, and see how you and/or your company can support the cause, by visiting **BigBrainClub.com**.

Thank you very much!
Dom Testa

MindBender 98: Pair of underwear

Answers

to Bonus Questions from Volume 1

Many thanks to everyone who purchased *The Mindbender Book Volume 1*. At the end of that book I included five bonus questions... without the answers. Now your patience is rewarded: here are the questions again, along with the answers:

1 47% of us do this ourselves, 39% have someone do it for us, and 14% never do it at all.

Answer: Wash our car

2 There will be about 31,557,000 of these this year.

Answer: Seconds (as in time)

3 Your average kid in America will eat 33 quarts of this each year.

Answer: Popcorn

4 79% of Americans use their lunch break from work to do this.

Answer: Actually eat their lunch...21% use the time for other things

5 One in twelve American women describe this as the biggest nightmare in their life.

Answer: Holiday shopping

MindBender 100: Their pet

More from Dom Testa

Non-fiction

The Mindbender Book, Volume 1

Smart Is Cool (coming 2013)

Fiction

The Comet's Curse

The Web of Titan

The Cassini Code

The Dark Zone

Cosmic Storm

The Galahad Legacy

Stay connected to Dom

DomTesta.com

Facebook.com/DomTesta

Twitter: @HeyDomTesta